Let's Visit the Pet Shop

A Hello Reader! Activity Book

ISBN 0-590-53746-6

Written by Sonia W. Black
Illustrated by Joan Holub

12 11 10 9 8 7 6 5 4 3   6 7 8 9/9 0/0

Printed in the U.S.A.   23

First Scholastic printing, June 1995

SCHOLASTIC INC.
Cartwheel BOOKS®

New York   Toronto   London   Auckland   Sydney

A Pet for Pam and Ben!

Ben and Pam want a pet. Help them get to the pet shop. Find the right path.

At the Shop

These two pictures are not the same. Circle five things that are different on this page.

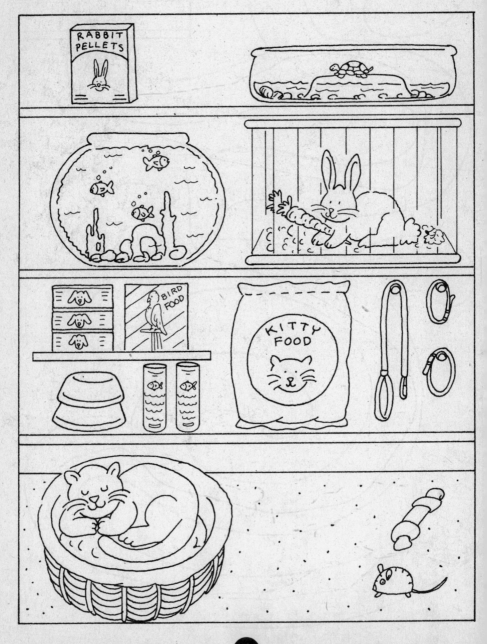

Dot-to-Dot Animals

Maybe *this* will be their pet. Connect the dots from A to Z and see.

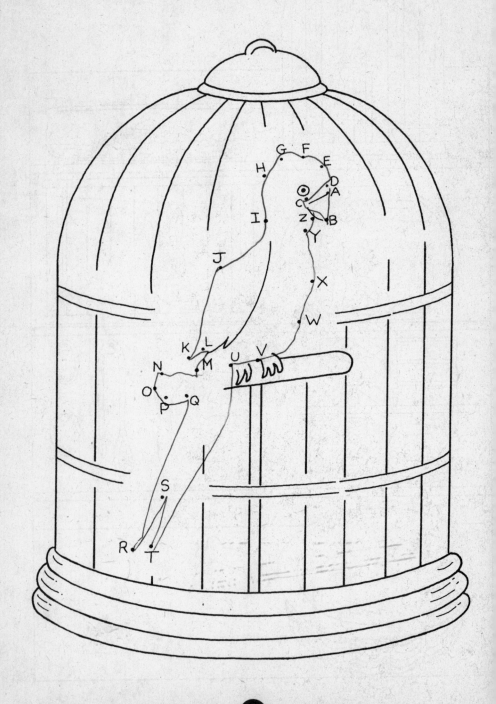

And What Animal Is This?

Find out. Connect the dots from A to Z.

Puppy Love

Put an X on the biggest puppy. Put a circle around the smallest puppy.

Scruffy Puppy

Pam likes the scruffy puppy. Can you make the scruffy puppy pretty? Put the pictures in the right order. Number them from 1 to 4.

Picture-Clue Crossword

Fill in the names of the animals. Use the picture clues.

ACROSS

#2.

#5.

DOWN

#1.

#3.

#4.

Which animal makes these sounds? Use the picture clues. Write the number in the space.

A. Animal #_____ says MEOW!

B. Animal #_____ says HISS!

C. Animal #_____ says WOOF WOOF!

D. Animal #_____ says SQUEAK SQUEAK!

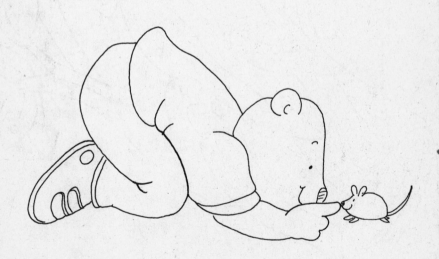

·············· Hide and Seek ················

Ben sees an animal that he likes. Do you want to
see it? Color in all the spaces with the letter "b."

Feeding Time!

The animals have to be fed. Draw a line from the animal to the food it eats.

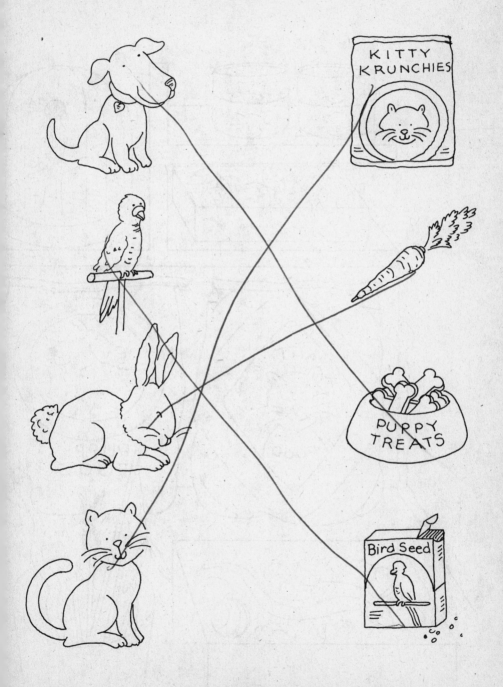

········ **Where Are the Snakes?** ········

"**Y**ikes!" cries Pam. Five garden snakes are missing!
Can you find them? Color each snake green.

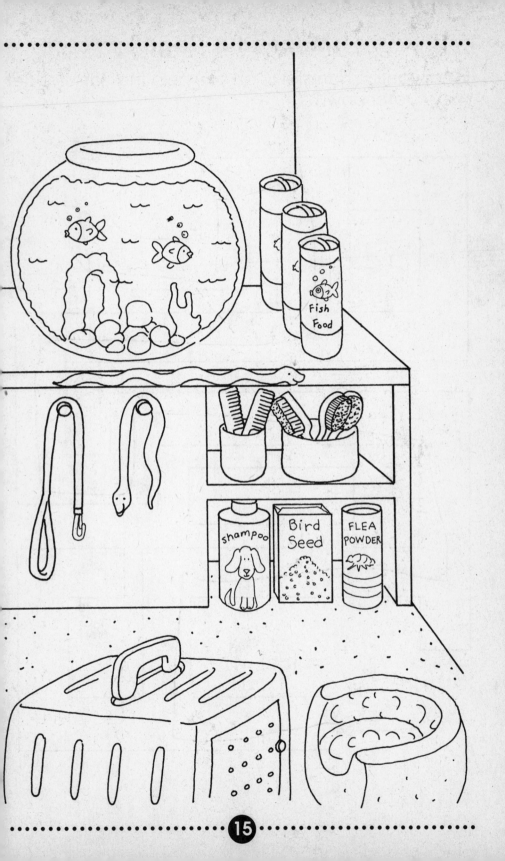

Ben wants a hamster. Can you help the hamster get to his water bowl?

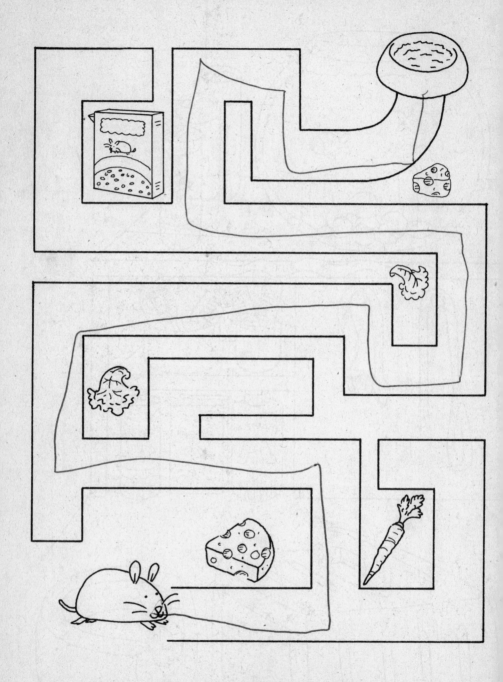

Turtles and Fish

"I like fish," says Pam. "I like turtles," says Ben. Put an X on each fish. Circle each turtle.

Purr-fect Kittens

Will Pam and Ben get a cute kitten? Color this picture any way you like.

Find the Difference

"There are too many animals to choose!" says Pam. One animal in each row is different from the others. Circle the animals that are different.

Draw the pet that *you* think Pam and Ben should get!

Answers

Page 2: A Pet for Pam and Ben!

Page 8: Puppy Love

Page 4: At the Shop

Page 9: Scruffy Puppy

Page 6: Dot-to-Dot Animals

Page 10: Picture-Clue Crossword

Page 7: And What Animal Is This?

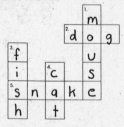

Page 11: Sound Off!

A. #4
B. #5
C. #2
D. #1

•••••••••••••••••••Answers••••••••••••••••••••

Pages 12: Hide and Seek

Page 13: Feeding Time!

Page 14: Where Are the Snakes?

You should have colored these <u>five</u> snakes.

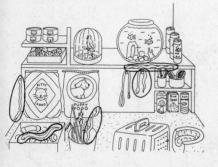

Pages 16: Maze in a Cage

Pages 17: Turtles and Fish

Pages 20: Find the Difference

_____

(your name)

did a great job!